String
Bass
98SB

Deborah Baker Monday & Janice L. McAllister

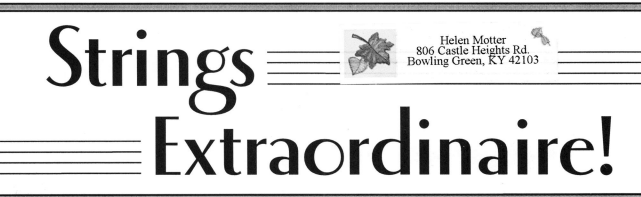

Helen Motter
806 Castle Heights Rd.
Bowling Green, KY 42103

Strings Extraordinaire!

Performance Ensembles – A Multi-Level Approach
Edited By Robert S. Frost

Strings Extraordinaire! is a progressive collection of classical, traditional, folk, and original performance pieces which provides a quality musical experience for students of different playing levels. Each piece is scored with an advanced, (A), and beginning, (B), part for violin, viola, cello, and bass. The violin/viola and cello/bass parts are correlated for ease in teaching. An optional piano accompaniment part is also provided. The pieces found in **Strings Extraordinaire!** were selected for their suitability for programs early in the school year, during the mid-year and holiday season, and those culminating with end-of-the-year concerts.

TABLE OF CONTENTS

D1275190

ISBN 0-8497-3389-8

©1999 **Neil A. Kjos Music Company**, 4380 Jutland Drive, San Diego, California, 92117.
International copyright secured. All rights reserved. Printed in U.S.A.
WARNING! The contents of this publication are protected by copyright law. To copy or reproduce them by any method is an infringement of the copyright law. Anyone who reproduces copyrighted matter is subject to substantial penalties and assessments for each infringement.

2

A reel is a lively dance which originated in Scotland many centuries ago. In North America, it is known as a hoedown and is a favorite type of music found at square dances.

Play *Harvest Reel* with "energized" bow strokes. Part A: Measures 8–12 should be played entirely in 3rd position. As you shift up and down, allow your hand to smoothly move to the new position. Avoid gripping the neck of your bass.

Harvest Reel

Monday

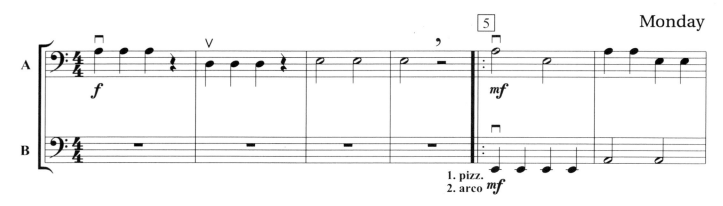

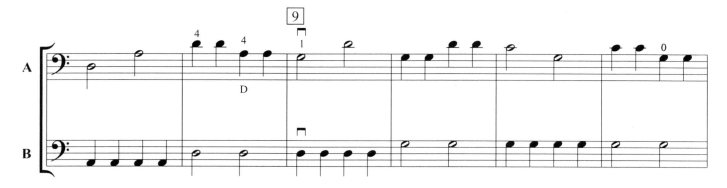

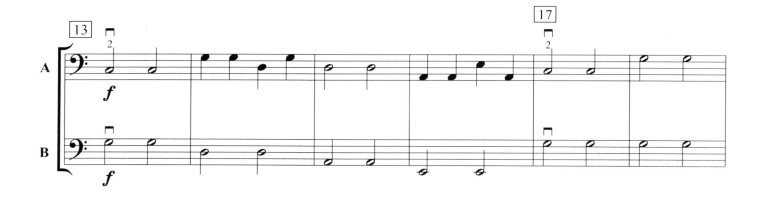

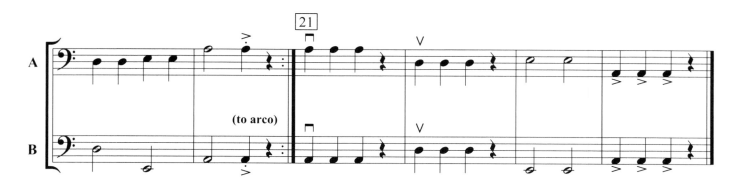

©1999 Neil A. Kjos Music Company, 4380 Jutland Drive, San Diego, California, 92117.

The *Largo* melody is from the ninth symphony of Czech composer Antonín Dvořák (1841–1904). He wrote this ninth symphony during his three-year stay in America. Many believe Dvořák was inspired by the folk-like music of the American slaves as well as music from his homeland. The *Largo* is from the 2nd movement of that symphony.

Play with long, legato bow strokes. Practice playing from very soft to loud by increasing bow weight and changing bow speed as you get louder. If you are learning vibrato, use it in this piece to enrich your tone.

Largo

from Symphony No. 9 "From the New World"

Dvořák / Monday

©1999 Neil A. Kjos Music Company, 4380 Jutland Drive, San Diego, California, 92117.

4

This melody features the augmented second interval (G♯ down to F) and it is characteristic of music from the Middle East. Part A: The alternate fingerings in measure 5 – 7 are to be played in ½ position. The dotted line means to hold down the 2nd finger. All players must have a secure bow hold to produce a good marcato-style bowing.

Tumba

Palestinian Folk Song

Monday

©1999 Neil A. Kjos Music Company, 4380 Jutland Drive, San Diego, California, 92117.

This English tune first appeared in print in 1728 but didn't become well known until the 20th century when Australian-born composer Percy Grainger (1882–1961) used the melody for an orchestral piece by the same name. Strive to achieve a bright and cheerful sound when playing this dance tune.

Country Gardens

English Folk Song

Monday

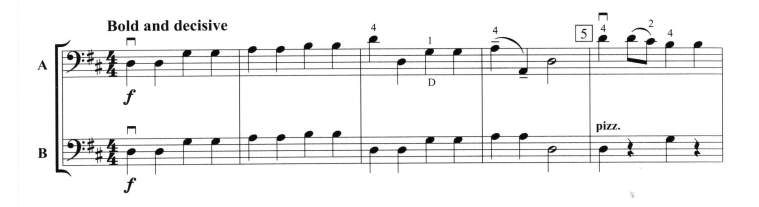

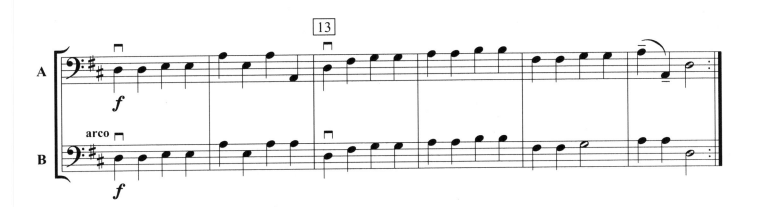

©1999 Neil A. Kjos Music Company, 4380 Jutland Drive, San Diego, California, 92117.

6

Known as the father of the modern symphony, Franz Joseph Haydn (1732–1809) was a popular and successful composer during his day. Haydn spent 30 years of his life working at the court of Hungarian Prince Esterhazy and composed music to be performed in the court for all occasions. This stately dance should be played like a slow waltz. Use staccato bow strokes.

German Dance

Haydn/Monday

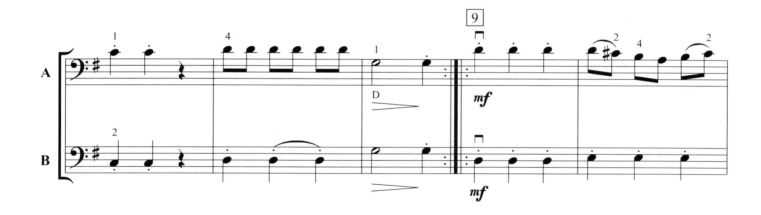

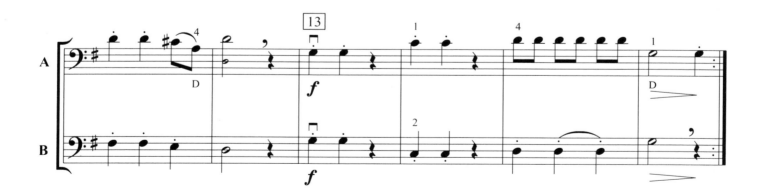

©1999 Neil A. Kjos Music Company, 4380 Jutland Drive, San Diego, California, 92117.

This old Netherlands song has become a traditional Thanksgiving hymn in America. The beautiful melodic line requires smooth bow changes. Part A: Use a light bow stroke on the up bow notes on the third beat of each measure. This will help the music to flow smoothly without unwanted accents.

We Gather Together

Netherlands Folk Song

Monday

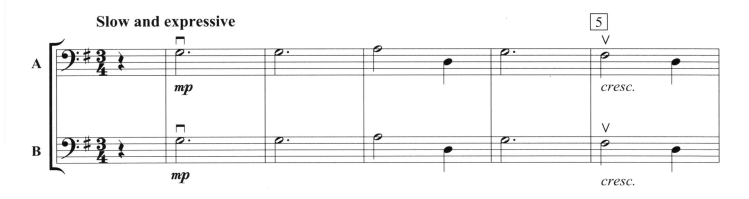

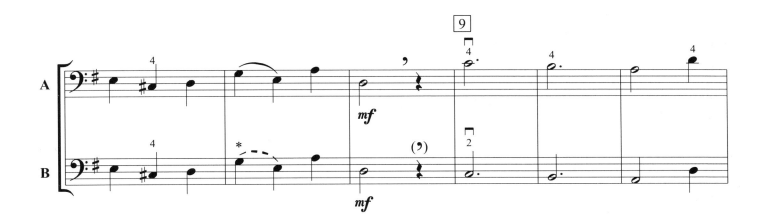

* Optional slur.

©1999 Neil A. Kjos Music Company, 4380 Jutland Drive, San Diego, California, 92117.

Johann Schop (1590–1667) was a German composer and instrumentalist. While there is not much information about him, he did leave several noteworthy sacred compositions. This chorale offers a wonderful opportunity to develop good intonation. Listen carefully to hear how your note fits into the chord played by the ensemble.

Chorale

Schop/McAllister

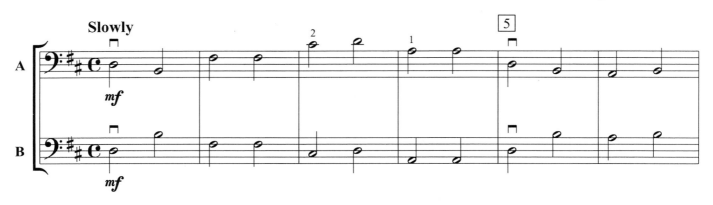

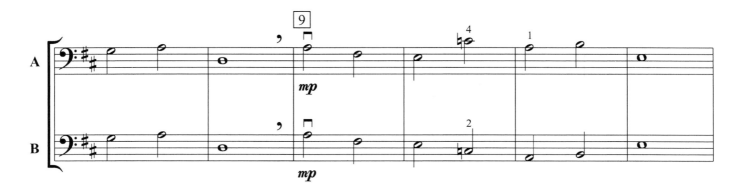

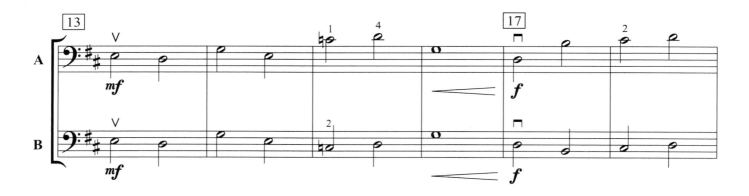

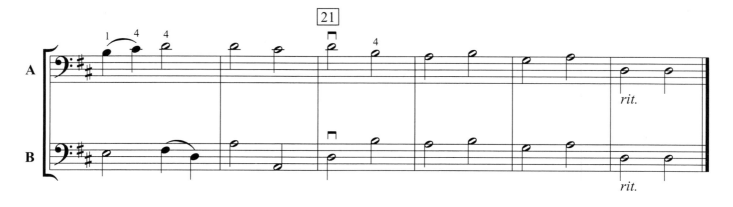

©1999 Neil A. Kjos Music Company, 4380 Jutland Drive, San Diego, California, 92117.

This processional is one of a group of pieces in a suite called *Water Music.* It was composed in 1717 by George Frideric Handel (1685–1759) for a royal water pageant which took place on the Thames River in England. One boat held a 50-piece orchestra and another for the royal party. Spectators and listeners also rode in boats and barges to see the spectacle and hear the music.

Processional

from Water Music

Handel/Monday

©1999 Neil A. Kjos Music Company, 4380 Jutland Drive, San Diego, California, 92117.

98SB

10

Special effects in music can be fun. Tremolo, meaning to tremble, is made with a fast back and forth movement in the upper part of your bow. With the help of your teacher, add tremolos to the accented half notes to create a spooky sound.

Goblin Walk

Monday

©1999 Neil A. Kjos Music Company, 4380 Jutland Drive, San Diego, California, 92117.

A *Gavotte* is a 17th century French dance in $\frac{4}{4}$ time played at a moderate tempo. Baroque-period composers such as Handel enjoyed including gavottes in their instrumental music. Play *Gavotte*, keeping the eighth notes smooth and the quarter notes slightly separated.

Gavotte in D

from Sonata #2 for Two Violins, Op. 5

Handel/McAllister

©1999 Neil A. Kjos Music Company, 4380 Jutland Drive, San Diego, California, 92117.

98SB

Jeremiah Clarke (c1674–1707) was a prominent English composer and organist. He composed church music, songs, music for the theater, and special pieces for the English Royalty. *King William's March* is an entrance march, written for King William III of Orange.

King William's March

Clarke/McAllister

©1999 Neil A. Kjos Music Company, 4380 Jutland Drive, San Diego, California, 92117.

Christmas Extraordinaire!

Secular and sacred music celebrating Christmas and wintertime have been written and performed for many centuries. The traditional Christmas carol has been one of the most popular types of music chosen to tell stories and express sentiments relating to this special time of year. The carol, however, did not originate as Christmas music. Many centuries ago, carols were based on dance music which were a part of village festivals, weddings, and birthdays. In the Middle Ages, carols were included in mystery plays which were often dramatizations of biblical stories. In the 16th century as the carol continued to develop and evolve, words were added and carols became more a part of the celebration of Christmas. The emphasis was to encourage congregational singing and this led to more widespread familiarity and recognition. Combining folk melodies with sacred words in many of them also helped to increase their popularity. Five carols have been selected to represent different moods and meanings of Christmas. They come from America, England, France, and Ukraine.

14

Jingle Bells, by James Pierpont (1822–1893), was copyrighted in 1857 in America under the title *One Horse Open Sleigh*. Copies sold for 2½ cents. Two years later, the song was republished under the title *Jingle Bells*. To create a bell-like sound with your instrument, play with short, stopped bow strokes.

Jingle Bells

Pierpont/Monday

©1999 Neil A. Kjos Music Company, 4380 Jutland Drive, San Diego, California, 92117.

This popular carol originated in France. It was included in a collection of carols published in 1700 by Bernard de la Monnoye, a French poet and scholar. It is thought that he wrote both the music and the words, adapting an ancient melody to sound like flutes over a bagpipe-like drone. Part B: Think of your part as imitating a drum.

Pat-A-Pan
French Carol

Monday

French carols are called "Noëls" and are among the oldest of carols. They date back to Medieval times when singing, dancing, and playing instruments were part of many ceremonies. *Ding Dong, Merrily on High*, from the 16th century, is partnered with the 18th-century carol, *il est ne, le divin enfan (He Is Born, The Child Divine)*. Use accents in the first carol to help the music sparkle. As you play, make each down and up bow accent sound just the same.

Two French Carols
Traditional

McAllister

 ©1999 Neil A. Kjos Music Company, 4380 Jutland Drive, San Diego, California, 92117.

Gently (Musette)

Tempo I

allargando = to slow down and crescendo at the same time.

The melody of this old English air is also known as *Greensleeves*. It became well known to Shakespeare theatergoers as he included *Greensleeves* several times in various plays. In the mid-1800s, it was sung as a Christmas carol with words added by Englishman William Dix. Part A: Smooth bow changes and solid bow weight will help provide a beautiful rich tone and legato sound for this melody. For those of you learning vibrato, use it!

What Child Is This?

English Carol

McAllister

98SB

©1999 Neil A. Kjos Music Company, 4380 Jutland Drive, San Diego, California, 92117.

Also called *Ukrainian Bell Carol*, this quick-moving piece suggests the sounds of church bells or chimes.
When accented notes appear in your part, imitate the striking of a bell with a quick "bite" and movement
of the bow.

Carol of the Bells

Ukrainian Carol

Monday

©1999 Neil A. Kjos Music Company, 4380 Jutland Drive, San Diego, California, 92117.

98SB

This joyous song is often sung following Jewish wedding ceremonies and offers the bride and groom good luck and fortune. Play with lots of energy by using short, yet strong bow strokes, especially when you have eighth notes.

Simon Tov

Israeli Folk Song

McAllister

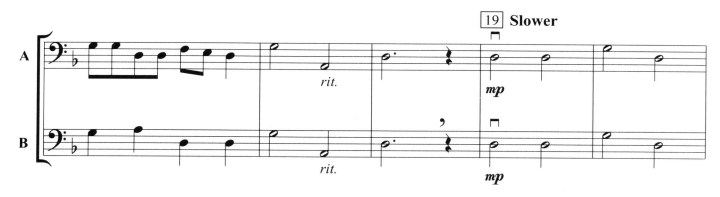

©1999 Neil A. Kjos Music Company, 4380 Jutland Drive, San Diego, California, 92117.

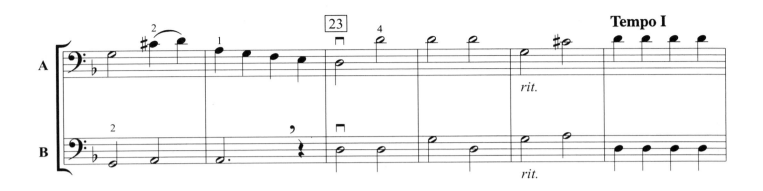

Two fiddling favorites are included here: *Soldier's Joy* and *Turkey in the Straw*. Everyone needs to play in the middle of the bow with short, crisp bow strokes. When learning the rhythms (especially the pattern in m.3), practice slowly at first as you clap and count aloud, then gradually speed up the tempo.

Fiddler's Frolic

Traditional

McAllister

©1999 Neil A. Kjos Music Company, 4380 Jutland Drive, San Diego, California, 92117.

BASS

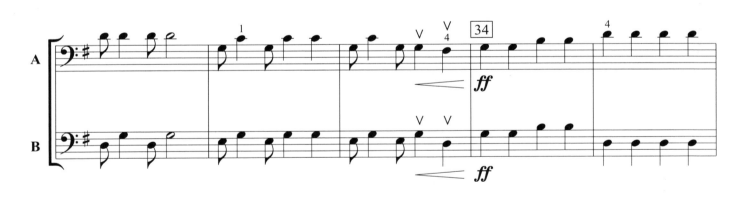

24

This upbeat Puerto Rican folk song meaning *How Beautiful Is the Flag*, reflects the spirit of Latin America. It includes syncopation which requires careful counting and exact rhythmic playing. Clap the rhythms allowing your entire body to feel the syncopation, then play them on your instrument.

Que Bonita Bandera

Puerto Rican Folk Song

Monday

©1999 Neil A. Kjos Music Company, 4380 Jutland Drive, San Diego, California, 92117.

26

Johann Pachelbel (1653–1706) was very successful as an organist throughout his life and was quite prolific as a composer. He wrote for the organ, harpsichord, as well as for vocal and chamber ensembles. The most popular of his works is *Canon*, a chamber music work originally composed for three violins and basso continuo. It features a set of 28 variations played by the violins over a recurring "ground" of two measures played by the bass instruments. This arrangement features 14 variations.

Canon

Pachelbel/McAllister

©1999 Neil A. Kjos Music Company, 4380 Jutland Drive, San Diego, California, 92117.

98SB

Hava Nagila, meaning *Come Let's Rejoice*, is a popular song from the Jewish tradition. The melody features the augmented second interval (G# down to F) in a similar manner as *Tumba* (page 4). Watch and listen very carefully as your teacher directs a gradual accelerando from the beginning to measure 21.

Hava Nagila

Israeli Folk Song

Monday

©1999 Neil A. Kjos Music Company, 4380 Jutland Drive, San Diego, California, 92117.